Story by

Tara Rossi
Tracy Mathison
Heidi Schoeneck

Illustrated by

Leah Roszkowski

www.sheshouldrun.org

Third Edition: October 2017

I dedicate this book to:

_____

_____

_____

_____

_____

_____

Meet Dick.
Dick is a Congressman.

This is also Dick.
This Dick is an Alderman.

LOOK! Another Dick!
This Dick is on city council.

There are a lot of
Dicks in office.

Meet Joan.
Joan is active
in her community.

Joan is a leader at work.

Joan is a great mother.

This is Bob and Sue.

They think Joan would
be great in government.

"Run, Joan, run,"
say Bob and Sue.

Joan always
wanted to run
for office.

But Joan is
not a Dick.

Is there room for Joan
in a world of Dicks?

Bob says, "There are too
many Dicks in office."

"Run, Joan, run!" says Sue.

See Joan run.

See Joan win.

See Joan make
a difference.

Do you know a Joan?
Should she run?

SHE SHOULD RUN.

You Ask. She Runs.
We All Win.

When women run for office, they are elected at the same rate as men. Yet less than a third of the United States' elected leaders are women.

Now is the time to bring more diverse voices to the table. Sharing this book is a great first step to inspire a woman to run for office.

Be Part of the Solution

She Should is on a mission to change the face of government. From running for school board or state senate, to encouraging women to do just that, help us get 250,000 women running by 2030. Join us and support the next generation of women leaders at www.SheShouldRun.org/250kby2030. #250Kby2030 #SeeJoanRun #SheShouldRun

She Should Run is a non-partisan
501(c)3 organization inspiring more
women and girls to run for elected office.